**Doob, Leonard W**
**A crocodile has me**
**by the leg**

9786

Poems translated from native African languages (and slightly changed in some cases so as to make them more easily understood), many about children or addressed to children. Arranged in classes: Mother and child, Good advice, Hunger, Two good insults, Songs to sing and dance to, and The sorrows of death. Bold black and white woodcuts by an African artist. For the special audience and mature reader.

# A CROCODILE HAS ME BY THE LEG

# A CROCODILE

# AFRICAN POEMS

# HAS ME BY THE LEG

EDITED BY LEONARD W. DOOB

*Illustrated by Solomon Irein Wangboje*

WALKER AND COMPANY

NEW YORK

# PREFACE

Poetry is the music in words and thoughts. It can make you laugh so much that you begin to bubble all over. Or it can make you want to cry when it tells you about yourself, about other people, about living and dying. You discover something which you did not know before or which, although it may have been deep inside, you were not able to talk about.

Here in this book are poems that bring fun. They are alive and lively. They are poems which Africans many years ago put together not as part of a book but as verses to be sung or spoken aloud when someone is feeling satisfied or feeling frightened. Some will make you happy. Others will make you sad. They will show you that Africans, even though they are far away and not living the kind of life you lead, are like yourself. All of us are different, all of us are the same.

The drawings, too, are part of Africa because they spring out of the eager mind of a Nigerian artist. They will give you new ideas about the poems. They will also make you learn more about Africa and Africans.

Perhaps you may wish to know where we found the poems. First travellers and scholars heard them in Africa and wrote them down in an African language. Then they were put into English or some other language. I have changed them here and there so that they could be more easily and quickly understood. But the original message of the unknown African poet is, I hope, expressed in the way he might have wanted you to receive it. Anyone wanting to know exactly where the poems come from should turn to the list at the end of this book.

L. W. D.

## BLESSINGS UPON AN INFANT

Hail, let happiness come:
The stranger has arrived,
His back is towards the darkness,
His face is towards the light.

May he work for his father,
May he work for his mother,
May he not steal,
May he not be wicked.

The children of this family
Forgive everything that can be forgiven.
May he eat by the work of his five fingers,
May he come to respect the world.

Why do you cry?
You are the child of a yam farmer,
Why do you cry?
You are the child of a cocoyam farmer,
Why do you cry?

Someone would like to have you for her child,
But you are my own.
Someone wishes she had you to nurse on a good mat,
Someone wishes you were hers.
She would put you on a camel blanket,
But I have you to rear on a torn mat.
Someone wishes she had you,
But it is I who have you.

**H**ush, my child,
Never mind, never mind.
Hush, my child,
Never mind, never mind.
There is a busybody gossiping,
There is a busybody gossiping.
Ho! we reap the maize.

**B**e still, my child,
Do you see those birds
In the tree?
If you cry,
A little bird
Is going to carry you off.


**B**e quiet, my baby,
Be still, my child,
Your mother has gone to get green mealies,
Your sisters are all gone gathering wood,
So be quiet, baby, be still.
Your father has gone awalking,
He has gone to drink good beer,
So be quiet, baby, be still.

If your mother has set out to fish,
I shall watch over you,
For she will give me a prawn.
If your mother has gone to crush corn,
I shall watch over you,
For she will give me a share of the pudding.
But if your mother has sallied forth to drink,
I shall abandon you to the ants,
For upon her return she will be tipsy
And not think about me.

## DITTY FOR A CHILD LOSING HIS FIRST TOOTH

He who has lost a tooth,
Cannot eat salt:
Come, give me palm oil
To eat with my corn.

I do not want the teeth of a pig,
They are big.
I want the teeth of a goat,
They are small.

**M**other dear,
Mother, who freely gives of what she has:
Fresh food and cooked meals alike.
Mother, who never deserts the hearth,
Mother, hearken to me!
The crying child will call after its mother.
How is it that mother does not answer me when I call?
Are we quarreling?

# GOOD ADVICE

# SONG FOR
# THE LAZY

If you are hungry
Use your hoe,
The only drug
The doctors know.

Never get up till the sun gets up,
Or the mists will give you a cold.
And a parrot whose lungs have once been touched
Will never live to be old.

Never eat plums that are not quite ripe,
For perhaps they will give you a pain;
And never dispute what a hornbill says
Or you will never dispute again.

Never despise the power of speech;
Learn every word as it comes.
For this is the pride of the parrot race,
That it speaks in a hundred tongues.

Never stay up when the sun goes down,
But sleep in your own home bed.
And if you have been good, as a parrot should,
You will dream that your tail is red.

Young lady,
Look for some medicine:
You have been ill too long.
Get yourself some medicine,
So that someone will marry you.


If a jackal bothers you, show him a hyena,
If a hyena bothers you, show him a lion,
If a lion bothers you, show him an elephant,
If an elephant bothers you, show him a hunter,
If a hunter bothers you, show him a snake,
If a snake bothers you, show him a stick,
If a stick bothers you, show it a fire,
If a fire bothers you, show it a river,
If a river bothers you, show it a wind,
If a wind bothers you, show it God.

It is man who counts.
I call upon gold:
It answers not.
I call upon drapery:
It answers not.
It is man who counts.


I am rich
And I shall die;
You are poor
And you will die.

If we want to tell a lie,
Our eyes will be insistent and shifty.
If we want to tell the truth,
Our body will be quiet and peaceful.
A lie cannot be told face to face.


One thread of truth in a shuttle
Is stronger than a hundred threads of lies.
Vomiting one's liver cures the most severe biliousness;
The hatching of an egg is unpleasant for the shell:
Do not match yourself against Providence.
God is all-powerful:
He prevents the eye from seeing the eyelashes.
Eggs become grand roosters:
The small man becomes the great man.
Stick to the truth:
Truth is like the light of dawn,
Untruthfulness is like darkness at night.

See how the doves flutter and huddle,
Dismayed at the sight of the eagle:
Woe to the dove that has no wings.

Come here, my beloved,
Come, give me a kiss.
There is a new law
Which says we must embrace each other.


To become a chief's favorite
Is not always comfortable;
It is like making friends
With a hippopotamus.


No man exists
Who can lay hold of a wild elephant
And lead him around;
No man exists
Who can grip a lion by the nape of the neck
And give him a punch.

Hunger is bad,
Hunger is like a lion,
Hunger is bad,
It makes us eat locusts.


I do not know
What will happen to me
Regarding food,
What will happen to me,
Regarding food.
I do not know
What I shall do
To get something to eat.

This little cloud, and this,
This little cloud, and this,
Let the rains come
With this little cloud.
Give us water,
Our hearts are dry,
O Lord,
Give us water,
Our hearts are dry,
O Lord.

I have given up singing about men,
I am looking only for clouds,
The millet has withered in the field.
The world has gone from bad to worse,
We die like fools.

Rest under a tree and you rise no more.
By God, some day or other
Clouds appear and you say,
Perhaps it will rain today.
But the sun takes its walk through the sky,
And no rain comes down
To drive us into shelter.

When the sky is clear for days and days,
Even a fool then knows
That the world is undone.

We must overcome the east wind
Which brings no rain;
We crave rain,
Let showers pour,
Let rain fall;
If rain comes, then all is well.

If it rains and grain ripens, then all is well;
If children rejoice, then all is well;
If women rejoice, then all is well;
If young men sing, then all is well;
If the aged rejoice, then all is well;
If rain comes, then all is well.

May the wind veer to the south,
So that the torrents will flow;
May our grain fill the granaries,
May the granaries overflow;
If rain comes, then all is well;
If rain comes, then all is well.

You who cultivate fields,
Your merit is great,
Wealth flows from your fingers,
The sea gushes out in front of your house.
You share what you produce
With the begging cripple at your door:
For this you receive blessing.
You share what you produce
With the begging orphan at your door:
For this you receive blessing.
And so ants will not eat your fingers;
After you die, your destiny will be paradise,
As long as you live, you will be blessed.

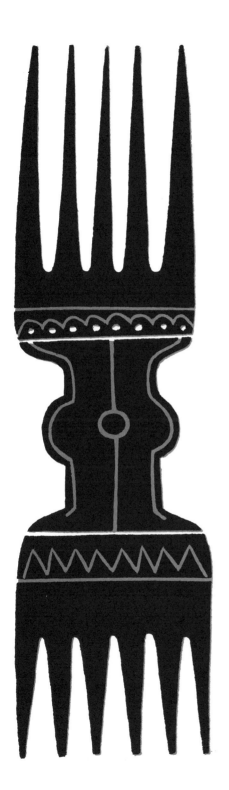

# TWO GOOD INSULTS

You really resemble
And old man who has no teeth
And who wants to eat elephant hide,
Or a woman without a backside
Who sits down on a hard wooden stool.
You also resemble a stupid dolt
Who while hunting lets an antelope pass by
And knows that his father is sick at home.

Woman, your soul is misshapen,
In haste was it made;
So fleshless a face speaks,
Saying your soul was formed without care.
The ancestral clay for your making
Was molded in haste.
A thing of no beauty are you,
Your face unsuited for a face,
Your feet unsuited for feet.

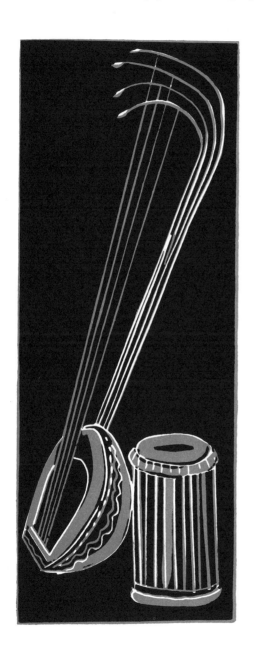

## SEVERAL GIRL'S SONGS

**W**hen I asked for him at Entoto, he was towards Akaki,
So they told me;
When I asked for him at Akaki, he was towards Jarer,
So they told me;
When I asked for him at Jarer, he was at Mendar,
So they told me;
When I asked for him at Mendar, he was towards Awash,
So they told me;
When I asked for him at Awash, he was towards Chercher,
So they told me;
When I asked for him at Chercher, he was towards Harar,
So they told me;
When I asked for him at Harar, he was towards Djibouti,
So they told me;
When I asked for him at Djibouti, he had crossed the sea,
Or so they said:
I sent to find him a hundred times,
But I never found him.
I sit by the fire and weep:
What a fool he is
To hope he will ever find anyone to equal me.

**C**ome, it is late in the day:
All those of my age are married,
And now I wander, wander all alone.
Hold back the sun that it may not go down
Without carrying the news of my bethrothal.


**L**onging pleases me like sweet fragrance,
Memory brings me pain.
I dreamt of a young man
Who would come to admire me
And not of a handsome stranger
Who would smile at me and pass by.

We mold a pot as our mothers did.
The pot, where is the pot?
The pot, it is here.
We mold the pot as our mothers did.

First, the base of the pot.
Strip by strip, and layer by layer.
Supple fingers kneading the clay,
Long fingers molding the clay,
Stiff thumbs shaping the clay,
Layer by layer and strip by strip,
We build the pot as our mothers did.

We build the pot as our mothers did.
Strip by strip and layer by layer.
Its belly swells like the paunch of a hyena,
Of a hyena which has eaten a whole sheep.
Its belly swells like a mother of twins.
It is a beautiful pot,
It swells like a mother of twins.

The far-off mountains hide you from me,
While the nearer ones overhang me.
Would that I had a heavy sledge
To crush the mountains near me.
Would that I had wings like a bird
To fly over those farther away.


I refused, of course I did,
I do not want to get married.
But father and mother compel me to,
And so I am willing to give it a try.


Coo-coo-roo of the girls,
Hopper in the sand;
They are playing behind the kraal,
They make short turns and little circles,
They make short turns and little circles again and again;
Coo-coo-roo, coo-coo-roo, coo-coo-roo-coo-coo.

# LOVE SONG FOR NNEKA

(Whose Name Means "Mother's Love Is Best")


Nneka, lovely damsel,
Beautiful Nneka;
Your teeth are as white as pearls,
Beautiful Nneka.

Nneka with body like bronze,
Beautiful Nneka;
Your hair is black and glossy,
Beautiful Nneka.

Nneka, lovely as the pelican,
Beautiful Nneka;
Nneka, I love you so,
Beautiful Nneka.

# PRAISE SONG FOR
# A DRUMMER

The drum drums health,
The drum drums wealth,
He takes his wife six hundred thousand cowries.
The drum drums health,
The drum drums wealth,
He takes his son six hundred thousand cowries,
The drum drums health,
The drum drums wealth.

## SONG OF YOUNG MEN WORKING IN GOLD MINES

Stones are very hard to break
Far from home, in a foreign land,
Far from home, in a foreign land,
Stones are very hard to break.

## HUNTER'S SONG

In the bush, in the deep forest,
We do our work;
One hunter digs a hole,
The other sets a trap.
We divide the meat with our followers,
Another part we cut in pieces
And dry over the fire.
We all die in the same way;
And so, hunters, let us be good comrades.

# MINSTREL'S SONG

There are, some people say, no riches in the bush.
But look at an ant hill:
It has a helmet providing shelter from the rain.
See that beetle:
His coat does not go around him
And yet it has three buttons.
A bird which lives there in the bush
Has a wooden house:
Who is the carpenter?
This bush cow wears boots
Like those of a soldier;
That baboon has a black coat
Like a policeman;
And the kingfisher has a silk gown.
Why, then, do some people say
There are no riches in the bush?

# SONGS PRODUCING COURAGE

### 1.

Friend, sweep away fear,
Dwell not among the fearful,
Be brave and fearless.
For who with fear
Has been saved by fear?
What brave man's life
Has been made brief
By bravery?
Outside the eyelid,
Let no tear of cowardice drop.

### 2.

Wonder not,
Children of men,
Wonder not
At the things
That are in this world,
Wonder not.

### 3.

Hail, let us die valiantly:
Only those stumble
Who fear the bend ahead.
Death is not a matter of choice,
But of necessity.

## SONGS IN PRAISE
## OF THE CHIEF

Into what would I like to change myself?
Into the knife with which the chief cuts his meat.
What would I like to become?
The cup from which the chief drinks beer.


O great chief:
Just as the remedy
For hot food is a calabash spoon;
And for the dangers of water, a canoe;
And for being seized with hunger, a milch cow;
And for cold, a blanket;
And for protection against a tornado, a large leather sheet,
So you, O great chief, are the remedy
Against all that annoys.


## SONG FOR SOMEONE
## WHO IS ABSENT

How cold is an empty room,
How sad a deserted house,
O, how melancholic is an empty room,
I roam around looking, looking.

## SONG OF AN UNLUCKY MAN

Chaff is in my eye,
A crocodile has me by the leg,
A goat is in the garden,
A porcupine is cooking in the pot,
Meal is drying on the pounding rock,
The King has summoned me to court,
And I must go to the funeral of my mother-in-law:
In short, I am busy.

# DANCE OF THE ANIMALS

I throw myself to the left,
I turn myself to the right,
I am the fish
Who glides in the water, who glides,
Who twists himself, who leaps.
Everything lives, everything dances, everything sings.

The bird flies,
Flies, flies, flies,
Goes, comes back, passes,
Mounts, hovers, and drops down.
I am the bird.
Everything lives, everything dances, everything sings.

The monkey, from bough to bough,
Runs, leaps, and jumps,
With his wife, with his little one,
His mouth full, his tail in the air:
This is the monkey, this is the monkey.
Everything lives, everything dances, everything sings.

# MORNING PRAYER

O Great Mountain, you chief,
Whom we live beside,
I recline, I am a gnat
But I would like to get up
And be an elephant.
O Sun, you chief,
Even as the Mountain remains immutable,
Your life undergoes no change.
Come, burst forth,
Let me shine like you, O chief.

# THE SORROWS OF DEATH

We wish to be joyful,
While we live, we wish to be joyful,
For in the grave we have nothing,
While we live, we wish to be joyful.
If I knew what to do
To ask for life,
Then I would ask for life.
If I had good palm wine to sacrifice,
Then I would go to the shrine of God
To beg for life;
If I had good water as a gift,
Then I would go to the shrine of the gods
To beg for life.


May the gravediggers not bury me,
May the gravediggers not bury me,
Let them bury my feet
But leave my body free,
That my friends may come to see my face,
That they may come and look upon my face.

# ACKNOWLEDGEMENTS

The editor is responsible not only for making minor or major changes in most of the verses for the sake of clarity but also for almost all of the retranslations from French and German. Grateful acknowledgment is made to the following persons who originally transcribed and translated the verses as well as to the publishers and journals which have given permission for their use. Poems are identified by first line and in the order in which they appear in the book.

"Hail, let happiness come," M. J. Field, Oxford University Press; "Why do you cry," J. H. K. Nketia, *Black Orpheus;* "Hush, my child," Margaret Read, *Bantu Studies;* "Be still, my child," Ch. Béart, *Mémoires de l'IFAN;* "Be quiet, my baby," E. J. Bourhill and J. B. Drake, Macmillan, (London); "If your mother has set out to fish," Ch. Béart, *Mémoires de l'IFAN;* "He who has lost a tooth," Melville J. Herskovits, Augustin; "Mother dear," Geormbeeyi Adali-Mortti, *Black Orpheus;* "If you are hungry," Dugald Campbell, Seeley Service; "Never get up," Akiki K. Nyabongo, Charles Scribner's; "Young lady," J. H. K. Nketia, University of Ghana; "If a jackal bothers you," D. W. Arnott, *Africa;* "It is man who counts," J. G. Christaller, Lutterworth Press; "I am rich," F. W. H. Migeod, Kegan Paul, Trench, Trübner; "If we want to tell a lie," J. D. Clarke, *Journal Royal Anthrop. Inst.;* "One thread of truth," J. R. Patterson, Government Printer (Nigeria); "See how the doves," A. C. Jordan, *Africa South;* "Come here, my beloved," Hugh Tracey, African Music Society; "No man exists," Enrico Cerulli, *Journal African Soc.;* "To become a chief's favorite," Hugh Tracey, *African Affairs;* "Hunger is bad," H. A. Fosbrooke, *Tanganyika Notes & Records;* "I do not know," Victor Lebzelter, Hiersemann; "This little cloud," R. S. Rattray, Society for Promoting Christian Knowledge; "I have given up singing," Hans Koritschoner, *Tanganyika Notes & Records;* "We must overcome the east wind," J. H. Driberg, T. Fisher Unwin; "You who cultivate fields," Wolf Leslau, *Africa;* "You really resemble," Gunter Tessmann, Ernst Wasmuth; "Woman, your soul is misshapen," Melville J. Herskovits, Augustin; "When I asked for him at Entoto," Sylvia Pankhurst, Lalibela House; "Come, it is late in the day," A. C. Jordan, *Africa South;* "Longing pleases me," Flavien Ranaivo, *Afrika Heute;* "We mold a pot," J. H. Driberg, Payson & Clarke; "The far-off mountains," A. C. Jordan, *Africa South;* "I refused," Herman Rehse, Strecker & Schröder; "Coo-coo-roo," D. F. v. d. Merwe, *Bantu Studies;* "Nneka," D. C. Osadebay, *African Affairs;* "The drum drums health," Mary Smith, Faber & Faber and Praeger; "Stones are very hard," Henri A. Junod, Macmillan (London); "In the bush," Hans Koritschoner, *Tanganyika Notes &*

*Records;* "There are, some say," K. L. Little, *Man;* "Friend, sweep away fear," Edward Steere, Society for Promoting Christian Knowledge; "Into what would I like to change myself," Bruno Gutmann, Evang.-Luth. Mission; "O great chief," J. R. Patterson, Government Printer (Nigeria); "How cold is an empty room," J. H. K. Nketia, University of Ghana; "Chaff is in my eye," Merlin Ennis, Beacon Press; "I throw myself to the left," Blaise Cendrars, Payson & Clarke; "O great mountain," Bruno Gutmann, Evang.-Luth. Mission; "We wish to be joyful," Paul Wiegräbe, *Afrika und Uebersee;* "May the gravediggers," Diedrich Westermann, Oxford University Press.

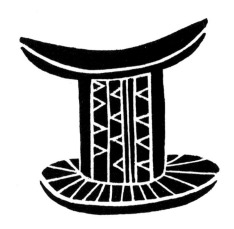